RICHARD STRAUSS • LIEDER-ALBUM I

Richard Strauss: Lieder-Album I

UE 5463 b
ISMN 979-0-008-01530-4
UPC 8-03452-00979-5
ISBN 978-3-7024-1226-5

Richard Strauss

Lieder-Album I
für mittlere Stimme mit Klavierbegleitung

English words by John Bernhoff

RICHARD STRAUSS
LIEDER–ALBUM

MORGEN!
TO - MORROW!

(John Henry Mackay)
The English Words by John Bernhoff

Für mittlere Stimme
For a medium voice

Richard Strauss, Op. 27, Nr. 4

Son - ne wie - der schei - nen   und auf dem We - ge, den ich ge - hen wer - de, wird
rise in glor - y beam - ing,   and in the path - way that my foot   shall wan - der, we'll

Universal Edition UE 5463 B

uns, die Glück-li-chen, sie wie-der ei - nen in-mit-ten die-ser son-nen-at-men-den
meet, for-get the earth, and lost in dream - ing, let heav'n unite a love that earth no more shall

Er - de..... und zu dem Strand, dem wei - ten, wo-gen-blau - en, wer-den wir
sun - der..... and towards that shore, its bil - lows soft-ly flow - ing, our hands en -

still und lang-sam nie-der-stei-gen, stumm
twined, our foot-steps slow-ly wend-ing, gaze

wer-den wir uns in die Au-gen schau-en, und auf uns sinkt des
in each o-ther's eyes in love's soft splen-dour glow - ing, mute with tears of

immer ruhiger, sempre più tranquillo

Glük-kes stummes Schwei-gen.....
joy and bliss ne'er end - ing.....

„DU MEINES HERZENS KRÖNELEIN"
"PRIDE OF MY HEART"

(Felix Dahn)
The English Words by John Bernhoff

Für mittlere Stimme
For a medium voice

Richard Strauss, Op. 21, Nr. 2

Du meines Her - zens Krö - ne-lein, du bist von laut - rem Gol - - de,
Pride of my heart, its crown, its joy, thou art a gold - en trea - sure;

wenn an - de-re da - ne-ben sein, dann bist du noch viel hol - de. Die
com - pared to thee, all is al - loy: none can thy vir - tues mea - sure. While

an - dern tun so gern ge-scheut, du____ bist gar sanft und stil - le, daß
o - thers boast with words of lore, thou____ art so meek and still, (sweet;) that

je - des Herz sich dein er - freut, dein Glück ist's, nicht dein Wil - le.
all thee in their hearts a - dore, thy charm 'tis, not thy will, (sweet.)

U. E. 5435ᵇ 5463ᵇ

MEINEM KINDE
TO MY BABY

(Gustav Falke)
The English Words by John Bernhoff

Für mittlere Stimme
For a medium voice

Richard Strauss, Op. 37, Nr. 3

U. E. 5459♭ 5463♭

U. E. 5459♭ 5463♭

Du schläfst und I
Thou sleepst and I

sach - te neig' ich mich über dein
bend me o'er thee, sweet, o - ver thy

Bett - - chen und seg - - - -
cra - - dle and a prayer - -

- ne dich.
re - rit. peat.

„WOZU NOCH, MÄDCHEN…"
"SAY, WHEREFORE VAINLY…"

(A. Fr. Graf v. Schack)

The English Words by John Bernhoff

Für mittlere Stimme
For a medium voice

Richard Strauss, Op.19, Nr.1

U. E. 5428♭ 5463♭

heim - nis von den Quel - len, den Blu - mengeistern längst er - späht; die
se - cret, sad dis - ast - er! they've told to brook and flow'- ret fair, the

dolce

Wo - gen murmeln's in den Grot - ten, es flü - stert's leis' der A - bendwind,
brook - let told it to the riv - er, 'tis whis-per'd low at day's re-treat,

dolce

wo du vor-bei-gehst, hörst du's spotten: wir wissen es seit lange, Kind!
which way thou turnest soft winds murmur: We know thy heart's fond secret, sweet!

Kind! Wo - zu noch, Mädchen, soll es frommen, daß du vor mir Ver-
sweet! Say, where fore, vainly wouldst dis-semble? Thine actions all thy

stel-lung übst?____
words dis - prove!____

sempre dim.

ZUEIGNUNG
DEVOTION

(Hermann v. Gilm)
The English Words by John Bernhoff

Richard Strauss, Op. 10, Nr. 1

Für mittlere Stimme
For a medium voice

Moderato.

Ja, du weißt es,
Ah! thou know'st, sweet,

teu - re See - le, daß ich fern von dir mich quä - le,
all mine an - guish, in thine ab - sence how I lan - guish.

Lie - be macht die Her - zen krank, ha - be Dank.
Love brings sor - row to the heart! Thanks, sweet heart!

con espress.

Einst hielt ich, der Frei - heit Ze - cher, hoch den A - me -
Once, when mer - ry songs were ring - ing, I to li - ber -

U. E. 5420♭ 7758♭

thy - sten=Be - cher   und du seg - ne-test den Trank,   ha - be Dank.
ty —   was drink - ing,   thou a bless - ing didst im - part.   Thanks, sweet heart!

con espress.

(religioso)
mit Weihe

Und be-schworst dar - in die Bö - sen,
Thou didst lay those want - on spir - its;

bis ich,   was ich nie__ ge-we - sen,   hei - lig, hei - lig ans Herz dir sank,
com-fort,   peace my soul__ in-her - its,   joy and bliss shall thy love im - part.

cresc.

ha - be Dank.
Thanks, sweet heart!

DIE NACHT
NIGHT

(Hermann v. Gilm)

The English Words by John Bernhoff

Richard Strauss, Op. 10, Nr 3

Für mittlere Stimme
For a medium voice

U. E. 5422♭ 5463♭

Al - les nimmt sie, was nur hold, nimmt das Sil-ber weg des Stroms,
Night steals all that we be-hold, e'en the sil-ver of the streams,

nimmt vom Kupfer-dach des Doms weg das Gold.
and from off the dome that gleams, steals the gold.

Aus-ge-plün - dert steht der Strauch, rük - ke nä - her, Seel' an See -
Bar-ren stand now bush and tree.— To my heart, o let me press

le; o die Nacht, mir bangt, sie steh - le
thee! lest (the) night's dark hand she should wrest thee,

dich mir auch.
sweet, from me.

FRÜHLINGSGEDRÄNGE
VOICES OF SPRING

(Nikolaus Lenau)
The English Words by John Bernhoff

Für mittlere Stimme
For a medium voice

Richard Strauss, Op. 26, Nr. 1

U. E. 5439♭ 5463♭

schmeicheln-den Wor - ten,   ru - fen hin-ein mit trunk' - nem Lär - men,
love's first ad - vent - ure;   shout - ing a - loud with wild re - joic - ing;

rüt - teln an längst ver-schloss' - nen Pfor - ten.
knock - ing at doors they ne'er can en - ter.

Früh - lings-kin - der,   mein Herz um-rin-gend,
Spring's sweet chil - dren,   with soft en - treat-ing,

was doch sucht ihr dar - in so drin-gend?   Hab' ich's ver -
seek ye the cause of my heart's loud beat-ing?   Have I be -

ra - ten euch jüngst im Trau - me, schlummernd un - term
trayed to you while I slum - ber'd, dream - ing 'neath your

Blü - ten-bau - me, brach - ten euch Mor - - gen -
blooms un - num - ber'd; did the south - wind, to

win - de die Sa - - - ge,
tell you, not tar - - - ry,

pp

daß ich im Her - - - - - zen ein - ge - schlos - sen
that in my heart's _____ deep hid - den cham - ber,

pp

18   U. E. 5439ᵇ 5463ᵇ

eu- -ren lieb-li-chen Spiel-ge-nos- -sen heim-
where your love-li-est play-mate reign- -eth, se-

- -lich und se- -lig
cret- -ed so fond- -ly,

ihr_____ Bild-nis tra- -ge?
love's im-age ___ I car- -ry?

dolce

pp

FÜR FUNFZEHN PFENNIGE

AND ALL FOR HALF-A-CROWN

(Aus „Feiner Almanach" des Knaben Wunderhorn)
The English Words by John Bernhoff

Fur mittlere Stimme
For a medium voice

Richard Strauss, Op. 36, Nr. 2

Lebhaft und lustig.
Vivo e giocoso.

Das Mägd - lein will ein' Frei - er hab'n, und sollt' sie'n aus der Er - de grab'n,
The maid would fain a lov - er find, to get one she had rack'd her mind,

_ für funf - zehn Pfen - ni - ge. Sie grub wohl ein, sie grub wohl aus und
_ and all for half - a - crown. She pon - der'd deep, left naught un - tried; at

grub nur ei - nen Schrei - ber her - aus _ für funf - zehn Pfen - ni - ge. Der
last a clerk with her wish com - plied, _ and all for half - a - crown. The

U. E. 5454♭ 5463♭

Er kauft ihr ei - nen brei - ten Hut,_____ der wär' wohl
He bought her many a broad-brimm'd hat,_____ to keep the

für die Son - - - ne gut, für fünf-zehn Pfen-ni - ge.
burn-ing sun_____ off, think of that! for half-a-crown.

Schreiber (zärtlich, schmachtend.)
Clerk (tenderly and languishing.)

Wohl für die Sonn', wohl für den Wind, bleib du bei mir,_____ mein lie - bes
Yea, for the sun, yea, for the wind, stay, stay with me,_____ be not un-

(sehr gefühlvoll)
(con molta espressione)

Kind_____ für fünf-zehn Pfen - - - - - ni - ge.
kind_____ I'll give thee half - - - - - a-crown.

U. E. 5454♭ 5463♭

Schreiber (ebenso rasch.)
Clerk (in the same manner.)

Dein' gu-ten Mut, den mag ich nicht, hast traun von treu-er
I would not wed thee, gen-tle dove, nay, by my troth, for

Lie-be nicht___ für fünf-zehn Pfen-ni-ge. Dein Herz ist wie ein
all thy love___ is not worth half-a-crown. Thy heart is like a

(mit größter Verachtung)
(with utmost contempt)

Tau-ben-haus, geht ei-ner 'nein, der and're aus___ für fünf-zehn
pig-eon-cot: new love flies in, the old flies out,___ it's not worth

Pfen-ni-ge.
half-a-crown.

U. E. 5454♭ 5463♭

„ACH WEH MIR UNGLÜCKHAFTEM MANN"

"AH, WOE IS ME, UNHAPPY MAN!"

(Felix Dahn)
The English Words by John Bernhoff

Richard Strauss, Op. 21, Nr. 4

Schel - len aus, daß du mich hört'st von Wei - tem, ich steckt' ein'n gro - ßen
sil - ver bells, that you should hear me com - ing; I'd wear a bunch of

Ro - sen-strauß an mei-ne lin-ke Sei - ten, und käm' ich an dein
ro - ses red, wet with the dew of morn - ing. Ar - riv-ing at your

klei - nes Haus, tät' ich mit der Peit - sche schla - gen;
cot - tage - door, I would crack my whip and dis - mount there;

da guck-test du zum Fen - ster
you'd ope' the win-dow then, and

U. E. 5437♭ 5463♭ 7758♭

ich nicht lan-ge war-ten kann, mei-ne Schimmel woll'ns nicht lei - - -
can-not tar-ry long, fare-well, for my hors-es would be start -

- - - - den.
- - - - ing.

Ach weh mir unglückhaftem Mann, daß ich Geld und Gut nicht
Ah, woe is me, un-hap-py man, neither gold, nor wealth, have

hab'.
I.

U. E. 5437♭ 5463♭ 7758♭

DIE GEORGINE
THE GEORGINA

(Hermann v. Gilm)
The English Words by John Bernhoff

Richard Strauss, Op. 10 Nr. 4

Für mittlere Stimme
For a medium voice

War-um so
Where fore so

spät erst, Ge - or - gi - ne? Das Ro - sen - mär - chen ist er - zählt und ho - nig-
late, say, sweet Geor-gi - na? The ro - se's fair-y - tales are told; and hon - ey-

satt hat sich die Bie - ne ihr Bett zum Schlum - mer aus - ge - wählt.
fed, long since the bee's flown to sleep and dream 'neath cells of gold.

Sind nicht zu kalt dir die - se Näch - te? Wie lebst du die - se Ta - ge
Are not the nights now cold and drear - y? How do you spend each lone - ly

hin? Wenn ich dir jetzt den Früh - ling bräch - te, du
hour? Shall I re-call sweet spring-time mer - ry, thou

feu - er - gel - be Träu - me-rin, wenn ich mit Mai - tau dich be - netz - te, be -
fier - y - yel - low, dream - ing flow'r, or shall with may - dew I re - fresh thee, or

gös - se dich mit Ju - ni-licht, doch ach, dann wärst du nicht die
warm thee with thee sun of June? But then thou wert not au - tumn's

Letz - te, die stol - ze Ein - zi - ge auch nicht.
glor - y, thou wouldst have blush'd and died too soon!

Wie,
Wake,

U.E 5423b 5463b

ICH LIEBE DICH
I LOVE BUT THEE

(Detlev von Liliencron)
The English Words by John Bernhoff

Für mittlere Stimme
For a medium voice

Richard Strauss, Op. 37, Nr. 2

U. E. 5458♭ 5463♭

vier trostlo - se Wän - - de, es kennt uns kein Hund.
ban - - ished and for - sak - - en, a crumbling hut our home.

ruhiger
più tranquillo

Steht sil - ber - be -
Be thy corse laid in

schla - gen dein Sarg am Al - tar, sie sol - len mich
mar - ble, Death's hand still near, I'd lie down be -

tra - gen zu dir auf die Bahr', und fern auf der
side thee and die on the bier. Shouldst die as a

U. E. 5458♭ 5463♭

Hei - de und stirbst du in Not, den Dolch aus der Scheide,
beg - gar, thy grave on the heath, my sword thro' my heart, love,

dir nach in den Tod!
I'd fol - low thee in death! -